Core Knowledge Language Arts®

Unit 8
Workbook

Skills Strand
KINDERGARTEN

Amplify learning.

Core Knowledge®

ISBN 978-1-61700-180-2

Printed in the USA
07 LSCOW 2020

Unit 8
Workbook

This Workbook contains worksheets that accompany many of the lessons from the Teacher Guide for Unit 8. Each worksheet is identified by the lesson number in which it is used. The worksheets in this book do not include written instructions for students because the instructions would have words that are not decodable. Teachers will explain these worksheets to the students orally, using the instructions in the Teacher Guide. The Workbook is a student component, which means each student should have a Workbook.

pond

ko pond

Directions: Have students copy the word on the line. Students should illustrate at least one meaning of the word.

rod

Directions: Have students copy the word on the line. Students should illustrate at least one meaning of the word.

Dear Family Member,

During this unit, your child will learn to read several words described as "Tricky Words." Although some letters in these words can be sounded out, other letters "do not follow the rules" your child has been taught for sounding out words. The letters not following the rules in a Tricky Word will be underlined in gray to remind you and your child it cannot be sounded out.

Today, your child learned the Tricky Words *the* and *a*. Help him practice these words by asking him to first read aloud the individual words and the sentences below. After reading each sentence ask him to say and circle Tricky Words. Then ask your child to write the Tricky Words on the lines below the sentence.

the   a

1. The cat is on the rug.

_____   _____
- - - - - - - - -   - - - - - - - - -
_____   _____

2. A man is on the bus.

_____   _____
- - - - - - - - -   - - - - - - - - -
_____   _____

3. The fish is in the pond.

_____   _____
- - - - - - - - -   - - - - - - - - -
_____   _____

4. Sam got <u>a</u> fish in th<u>e</u> net.

5. Th<u>e</u> king is glad he has <u>a</u> quilt.

6. Sam will bring <u>a</u> bag to shop.

7. Mom chats with th<u>e</u> kids.

8. Sam sang <u>a</u> song to th<u>e</u> kids.

Name _____

Dear Family Member,

Today your child learned the Tricky Words *of* and *all*. Help your child practice these words by asking your child to read the individual words in the box and the sentences below. After each sentence ask your child to say and write any Tricky Words from the sentence on the lines below.

| o̲f | a̲ll | the̲ | a̲ |

1. A̲ll o̲f the̲ kids munched chips.

_____ _____

_____ _____

2. Mom got Sam a̲ gift o̲f red pants.

_____ _____

_____ _____

3. Sam has a̲ll o̲f the̲ things in his box.

_____ _____

_____ _____

4. Mom, Dad, and Sam a̲ll had fish at lunch.

_____

- - - - - - - - - - - - - - - - - -

_____

5. Chad had <u>a</u> box <u>of</u> hats.

_____   _____

- - - - - - - - - - - - - - - - - -

_____   _____

6. The ships <u>all</u> got wet.

_____

- - - - - - - - - - - - - - - - - -

_____

7. <u>All</u> <u>of</u> <u>the</u> tots sang a song.

_____ _____ _____

- - - - - - - - - - - - - - - - - -

_____ _____ _____

8. Dad brings Sam <u>a</u> can <u>of</u> ham.

_____   _____

- - - - - - - - - - - - - - - - - -

_____   _____

Name _____

1. _____   _____

2. _____   _____

3. _____   _____

4. _____   _____

Directions: Have students copy and write each Tricky Word from memory.

snip

Directions: Have students copy the word on the line. Students should illustrate at least one meaning of the word.

snip

Dear Family Member,

Your child has been taught to read the Tricky Words *the*, *a*, *of*, and *all*. Tricky Words are difficult to read and spell because they do not follow the letter-sound correspondences your child has been taught. These tricky letters are underlined with a gray line. Tricky Words occur frequently in stories and need to be practiced often. Ask your child to cut out the word cards and arrange them to make phrases. Have your child read the phrases. Another way to practice: Arrange the cards yourself and have your child read the phrases. Please keep the cards for future practice.

of	the	a
all	ships	on
fast	mast	drift
wind	in	men

of	from	o<u>n</u>e

Directions: Have students write a word from the box to complete each sentence.

1. Stan got th<u>e</u> best gift
_____
_____ his mom.

2. Chad has six frogs and
_____
_____ dog.

3. Th<u>e</u> man had ham and <u>a</u>
_____
bag _____ chips.

of	one	all

4. Tim can crush a can with

_____

- - - - - - - - - - - - - - -

_____ hand.

5. The king slept on a bed

_____

- - - - - - - - - - - - - - -

_____ quilts.

_____

- - - - - - - - - - - - - - -

6. Stan had _____

the chips.

yelp

Name _____

chomp

_____
- -
_____

Directions: Have students copy the word on the line. Students should illustrate at least one meaning of the word.

Name _____

Dear Family Member,

    This is a story your child has read at school. Encourage your child to read the story to you, and then talk about it together. The tricky letters in the words are underlined in gray.

Sam and the Fish

This is Sam.

Sam and his dad fish in <u>a</u> pond.

Sam's dad brings <u>a</u> rod.

Sam brings <u>a</u> net.

Sam and his dad sit and sit.

Then, zap!

Sam's dad gets a fish.

The fish jumps.

The fish twists and swims.

Sam's dad tugs on the rod.

The fish swims past Sam.

Sam swings his net.

Sam lifts up the net.

The fish is in the net!

Sam and his dad grin.

task

trim

Directions: Have students copy the word on the line. Students should illustrate at least one meaning of the word.

shrub

Directions: Have students copy the word on the line. Students should illustrate at least one meaning of the word.

Dear Family Member,

This is a story your child has read at school. Encourage your child to read the story to you, and then talk about it together. The tricky letters in the words are underlined in gray.

Fun at the Pond

Sam is at the pond with his pals.

Six frogs rest in the wet mud.

Sam runs at the frogs.

The frogs all hop in the pond.

Sam's pal, Chad, digs up a crab.

The crab gets mad at Chad.

The crab snips at Chad's hands.

Chad drops the crab.

Jen lifts up a log and spots a bug.

The bug is long with lots of legs.

The bug runs and digs in the sand.

The pond is lots of fun.

Please ask your child to read the following phrases to you, paying special attention to the Tricky Words. If your child needs more practice with Tricky Words, please review the words with flashcards or have your child read the words several times.

1. the pond

2. one frog

3. a fish

4. all of the shrubs

5. lots of fun

6. one cat

7. a gift from Tim

8. all of the jobs from the list

Directions: Have students copy and write each Tricky Word from memory.

1.

2.

3.

4.

5.

6.

7.

Dear Family Member,

Your child has been taught to read the Tricky Words: *one*, *was*, and *from*. Tricky Words are difficult to read and spell because they have letters which do not follow the letter-sound correspondences your child has been taught. These tricky letters are underlined with a gray line.

Ask your child to cut out the word cards. Show the cards to your child and have your child read them. You may consider asking your child to make phrases with the cards and read them to you. Ask your child to copy the words onto a sheet of paper. Additional Activity: Read the words aloud and have your child write them down. Please keep the word cards for future practice.

pinch	hush	<u>a</u>ll
<u>of</u>	<u>one</u>	them
inch	jump	thump
next	w<u>a</u>s	fr<u>o</u>m

Directions: Have students copy and write each Tricky Word from memory.

1.

2.

3.

4.

5.

6.

7.

Dear Family Member,

This is a story your child has read at school. Encourage your child to read the story to you, and then talk about it together. The tricky letters in the words are underlined in gray.

Sam's Pets

Sam has pets.

One of his pets is a dog.

One of his pets is a cat.

One of his pets is a bug.

This is Sam's dog, Max.

Max runs and jumps.

Max digs in the mud.

Max rubs mud on Sam.

Max yelps at the cat.

This is Sam's cat, Tim.

Tim sips milk fr<u>o</u>m <u>a</u> dish.

Tim naps on Sam's bed.

Tim runs fr<u>o</u>m Max.

This is Sam's bug, King Tut.

King Tut hops fr<u>o</u>m plant to plant.

King Tut chomps on plants.

King Tut runs fr<u>o</u>m Tim.

Name _____

Dear Family Member,

This is a story your child has read at school. Encourage your child to read the story to you, and then talk about it together. The tricky letters in the words are underlined in gray.

Tasks

Sam has a long list of tasks.

Sam must scrub a bunch of cups.

Sam must help his dad trim shrubs.

Sam must mop the steps.

Sam scrubs all of the cups.

Scrub, scrub, scrub.

Sam helps his dad trim shrubs.

Snip, snip, snip.

The sun is hot.

Sam gets hot.

Sam spots <u>a</u> fan on the rug.

Sam flops on the rug and naps.

Then his mom spots him.

Sam's mom taps him with the mop.

Sam jumps up. Sam picks up the mop.

print

Directions: Have students copy the word on the line. Students should illustrate at least one meaning of the word.

quip

_____

- -

_____

Directions: Have students copy the word on the line. Students should illustrate at least one meaning of the word.

Name _____

Dear Family Member,

Your child has been taught to read words with double-letter spellings. We have included 'ck' with the double-letter spellings because both letters stand for the sound /k/. Similarly, in the word *puff,* both of the letters 'f' stand for the single sound /f/. Ask your child to cut out the word cards. Show the cards to your child and have your child read them. Extension: Read the words aloud and have your child write the sounds down, one at a time, paying attention to the double-letter spellings. Please keep the cards for future practice.

puff	buzz	hiss
quack	yells	fizz
class	mitt	eggs
sniffs	odd	thick

chills

_____
- -
_____

Directions: Have students copy the word on the line. Students should illustrate at least one meaning of the word.

Dear Family Member,

This is a story your child has read at school. Encourage your child to read the story to you, and then talk about it together. The tricky letters in the words are underlined in gray.

The Van

Sam's mom has <u>a</u> van.

Sam is in the van.

Sam and his mom got his pal, Chad.

Then the van hit <u>a</u> big bump.

The van will jump up, up, up.

Then, slam!

The van hit the land.

Crash!   Smash!   Crunch!

Snap!   Pop!

The van was bent.

The van had lots of dents.

The van did not run.

Sam's mom got a fix-it man.

The fix-it man had a big fix-it kit.

The fix-it kit did not help much.

The fix-it man did not fix the van.

Sam's mom got a cab.

The kids got in the cab.

Sam's mom was sad.

Sam held his mom's hand.

Then Sam sang his mom a song.

"Mom," Sam sang,

"a van is just a van!"

Dear Family Member,

Have your child read each of the Tricky Words below. After your child reads each word correctly, your child can color the box. How high can your child go in the rocket—all the way to the moon?!!

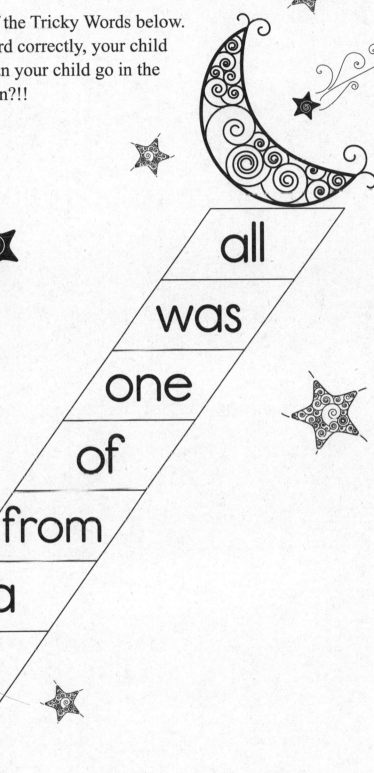

all

was

one

of

from

a

the

Dear Family Member,

This is a story your child has read at school. Encourage your child to read the story to you, and then talk about it together. The tricky letters in the words are underlined in gray.

On the Bus

The van is in the fix-it shop.

Sam's mom must get on the bus.

The bus pulls in at the bus stop.

Sam's mom gets on and sits in ba**ck**.

The bus bumps up the hi**ll**.

Sam's mom hangs on with <u>one</u> hand.

Sam's mom rings the bell.

The bus stops at the next stop.

Sam's mom gets off.

Summary Score Sheet

Teacher Directions: *Record the scores of each assessment on this sheet. Retain the sheet and the Assessment Worksheets completed by the student in the student's assessment portfolio.*

Student Performance Task Assessments required of all students

Word Recognition Assessment: _____/20

Lowercase Letter Name Assessment: _____/26

Tricky Word Assessment: _____/7

Individually Administered Assessments based on student performance

Pseudoword Reading Assessment: _____/30

Real Word Reading Assessment:_____/30

Code Knowledge Diagnostic Assessment:

　　Rows 1–5 ____/25

　　Rows 1–7_____/35

Story Reading:

　　Comprehension Questions: ____/3

　　Words Correct:_____

Recommendation: (Check One)

_____Continue to Units 9 and 10 for instruction.

_____Place in remediation group for instruction—do not continue to Units 9 and 10.

☺   run   leg   cup   cat

1.   med   mat   met   net

2.   rim   rot   rob   rod

3.   yes   yet   yez   yen

4.   hat   had   hid   ham

5.   gut   get   cot   got

6.   bad   pat   pit   pad

7.	sip	zip	sap	zap
8.	hen	ken	kin	jen
9.	vat	vet	fat	rat
10.	fax	fix	box	fox
11.	thin	fin	thick	this
12.	chill	jill	chin	still
13.	ships	chips	chops	shops
14.	chest	west	quest	quip

Name _____

15.	boss	bus	fuzz	buzz
16.	ebb	edd	egg	odd
17.	wick	wax	whips	wicks
18.	kin	king	kong	wing
19.	trip	drip	drop	drug
20.	shop	ship	shot	chop

Total Score: _____ /20

Notes:

Directions: For each word, have students circle and count the sounds. Have students write the number of sounds in the box and copy the word on the line.

1. sho**ck** ☐ _____

2. spe**ll** ☐ _____

3. **e**gg ☐ _____

4. cli**ff** ☐ _____

5. flu**ff** ☐ _____

6. splash ☐ _____

7. pinch ☐ _____

8. che**ck** ☐

9. clips ☐

10. fu**zz** ☐

11. dre**ss** ☐

12. ki**ck** ☐

13. plums ☐

14. grin ☐

1.	a	w	e	i
2.	t	y	u	w
3.	o	p	t	m
4.	f	g	h	n
5.	k	l	z	c
6.	c	b	v	d
7.	d	x	z	j
8.	n	i	h	m

9.   u   r   n   m

10.   l   y   p   g

11.   e   a   i   o

12.   n   h   m   k

13.   b   d   p   q

14.   i   l   t   f

15.   s   t   c   k

16.   x   s   t   z

17.   f   t   j   l

18.   y   i   j   g

Name _____

19.	i	e	u	j
20.	b	p	d	q
21.	z	s	c	t
22.	n	m	r	q
23.	q	u	w	d
24.	t	f	g	e
25.	c	b	v	d
26.	a	w	e	i

Total Score: _____ /26

Notes:

STUDENT RECORD SHEET - Pseudowords

If a student misreads a word, write what she says directly above the pseudoword.

1.	wug	rab	sep	zat	het
2.	kem	jid	pog	lum	yod
3.	lin	fod	cax	ved	mip
4.	nist	brin	clup	stent	glosp
5.	thog	shup	chim	quib	ling
6.	geck	vell	tass	beff	dagg

Total Score: _____/30

Notes:

STUDENT RECORD SHEET – Real Words

If a student misreads a word, write what she says directly above the word on the record sheet.

1. dog   bed   rat   him   but

2. yes   fax   cup   van   sad

3. let   rim   jot   zip   wag

4. step   drop   rust   bend   spent

5. then   shop   chin   quit   long

6. puff   back   egg   miss   fell

Total Score: _____/30

Notes:

sock rock	truck duck

_____

- - - - - - - - - - - - - - - -

_____

mitt kit	lock clock

_____

- - - - - - - - - - - - - - - -

_____

Directions: For each picture, have students circle and copy the matching word.

glass dress	drums plums

_____

- - - - - - - - - - -

_____

bell bill	egg eggs

_____

- - - - - - - - - - -

_____

Directions: Have students connect words that rhyme.

1.

2.

3.

4.

5.

6. bat   rat

7. bell   sell

8. chick   trick

9. tan   van

10. met   set

11. bring   thing

1.   u   up   a   the

2.   off   of   frame   from

3.   this   the   a   that

4.   waz   wet   with   was

5.   wab   ib   one   once

6.   from   off   up   of

7.   a   the   all   tell

dock

Directions: Have students copy the word on the line. Students should illustrate at least one meaning of the word.

peck

_____

- -

_____

Directions: Have students copy the word on the line. Students should illustrate at least one meaning of the word.

glint

_____

- -

_____

Directions: Have students copy the word on the line. Students should illustrate at least one meaning of the word.

STUDENT RECORD SHEET – Code Knowledge Diagnostic Assessment

Ask student for the sound of each letter. If he gives a letter name, remind him to provide the sound, not the name. Make a note of any letter for which the incorrect sound is given.

1. m   s   f   v   z

2. r   l   n   e   u

3. i   o   a   t   y

4. d   g   h   j   k

5. b   p   c   w   x

6. sh   ch   th   ng   qu

7. ff   ss   ll   gg   ck

Total Score: _____/35

Notes:

Dear Family Member,

Help your child practice the following Tricky Words. Ask him to first read each word in the box. Then ask him to use the words in the box to complete each sentence. You might suggest he cross out each word in the box as he uses it.

from	one	of	a	was	the	all

1. Sam just has ___one___ pet, not 2 pets.

2. ~~Sam had a bag~~ ___of___ chips at lunch.

3. Chad lost his ring and _____ sad.

4. Max is _____ dog.

5. Sam got his pack _____ his mom.

6. Sam and Chad went swimming in _____ pond.

7. The frogs _____ hop in the pond.

© 2013 Core Knowledge Foundation

The Chick

Sam and Chad got up on a rock.

On top of the rock was a gull's nest.

The gull had a chick.

Then the gull left.

The chick fell from the nest.

Plop!

The chick got stuck in a crack.

Sam and Chad got the chick.

Then Chad set it back in its nest.

Running Record for "The Chick"

Say to the student, "I have a story I want you to read aloud to me today. The title of the story is "The Chick." Can you tell me what you know about chicks?" (Allow the student time to tell you briefly what they may know about chicks. You do not need to record this information.)

"Now I am going to give you a copy of the story. I want you to read using your best reading voice and expression. I also want you to think as you read because I am going to ask you some questions at the end."

Read the title aloud to the student. Mark your running record as the child reads. Here are some easy common markings:

• circle omitted words
• line through mispronounced words and write what was said above the mispronounced word
• write TS (Teacher Supplied) above any word you had to supply to the student

The Chick

Sam and Chad got up on a rock.   (8)

On top of the rock was a gull's nest.   (17)

The gull had a chick.   (22)

Then the gull left.   (26)

The chick fell from the nest.   (32)

Plop!   (33)

The chick got stuck in a crack.   (40)

Sam and Chad got the chick.   (46)

Then Chad set it back in its nest.   (54)

Oral Comprehension Questions:

Where was the gull's nest?

What did the gull have in its nest?

Who got the chick and put it back in its nest?

✓ 1. shell

shell

✓ 2. duck

duck

✓ 3. mitt

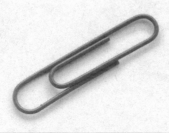

mitt

Directions: Have students write each word under its matching picture.

✓ 4. bell

~~bell~~ (crossed out)

bell

✓ 5. egg

egg

✓ 6. brick

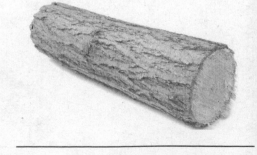

brick

Dear Family Member,

This is a story your child has read at school. Encourage your child to read the story to you, and then talk about it together. The tricky letters in the words are underlined in gray.

Stop That Bus!

Sam's mom runs in and yells,

"Sam, get up!"

Sam jumps up.

Sam's mom hands him his pants.

Sam jumps in his pants.

Sam's mom hands him his pa**ck**.

Sam slips the pa**ck** on his ba**ck**.

Sam's mom hands him his lunch.

Sam grabs it.

Sam and his mom run fast.

"That's the bus!" Sam yells.

Sam's mom huffs and puffs.

"Stop the bus!" Sam yells.

The kids on the bus spot Sam.

One of them yells, "That's Sam.

Stop the bus!"

The bus stops.

Sam is in luck.

Sam gets on the bus.

e**gg**	chi**ck**	so**ck**
be**ll**	gra**ss**	ki**ss**

_____

- - - - - - - - - -

_____

_____

- - - - - - - - - -

_____

_____

- - - - - - - - - -

_____

_____

- - - - - - - - - -

_____

_____

- - - - - - - - - -

_____

_____

- - - - - - - - - -

_____

| dress | buzz | clock |
| doll | cliff | mitt |

_____

- - - - - - - - - - - -

_____

_____

- - - - - - - - - - - -

_____

_____

- - - - - - - - - - - -

_____

_____

- - - - - - - - - - - -

_____

bzzzzzzzzzz

_____

- - - - - - - - - - - -

_____

Name _____

Dear Family Member,

This is a story your child has read at school. Encourage your child to read the story to you, and then talk about it together. The tricky letters in the words are underlined in gray.

Sam and the Duck

Sam's cla**ss** is on a trip.

The cla**ss** is at the do**ck**.

Mi**ss** Ma**ck** spots Ken, the fish man.

"Ken," Mi**ss** Ma**ck** asks,

"Can the kids dig in the sand?"

Ken nods.

"Yes, the kids can dig in the sand,

but the kids must not pet the du**ck**.

That du**ck** is a bad du**ck**.

That du**ck** pe**ck**s at kids."

Miss Mack tells the kids,

"Class, let's not pet the duck."

Sam and Chad dig in the sand.

Chad digs up a ring.

Sam lifts the ring up.

The ring glints in the sun.

The duck spots the ring.

The duck quacks and runs at Sam.

"Sam!" Miss Mack yells,

"It's that bad duck,

the one that pecks!"

The duck runs up and pecks

at Sam's hand.

Then it runs off with the ring.

"Man!" yells Chad.

"That is one bad duck!"

Directions: Have students circle the words read aloud and copy them on the lines.

1. hi**ll**   chi**ll**

2. flu**ff**   flip

3. si**ck**   lu**ck**

4. a**dd**   at

5. bu**zz**   fu**zz**

6. hi**ss**   bli**ss**

7. do**ll**   d**u**ll

8. cl**iff**   st**iff**

9. che**ck**   chi**ck**

10. mo**ss**   bo**ss**

11. o**dd**   o**ff**

12. fu**zz**   fu**ss**

1. buzz   drum

2. from   <u>o</u>ne

3. crack   leg

4. fun   w<u>a</u>s

5. egg   stack

Directions: Have students draw a line from each word on the left to the rhyming word on the right.

6. add   press

7. still   sock

8. dress   glad

9. cliff   thrill

10. clock   stiff

sni**ff**	frog
soft	pu**ff**
stu**ff**	gift
fresh	fist

as in <u>f</u>it

as in hu<u>ff</u>

_____

- - - - - - - - - - -

_____

- - - - - - - - - - -

_____

_____

- - - - - - - - - - -

_____

_____

- - - - - - - - - - -

_____

- - - - - - - - - - -

_____

do**ll**	long
lunch	belt
sti**ll**	spe**ll**
bi**ll**	lamp

as in l<u>i</u>p   as in hil<u>l</u>

Directions: Have students write the words containing the /l/ sound spelled 'l' under the 'l' header and the words containing the /ll/ sound spelled 'll' under the 'll' header.

Name _____

Directions: Have students write the words containing the /s/ sound spelled 's' under the 's' header and the words containing the /s/ sound spelled 'ss' under the 'ss' header.

class	sting
boss	moss
spot	pest
mess	pass

as in <u>s</u>top

as in to<u>ss</u>

_____

- - - - - - - - - - - - - - -

_____

_____

- - - - - - - - - - - - - - -

_____

_____

- - - - - - - - - - - - - - -

_____

_____

- - - - - - - - - - - - - - -

_____

mutt	stamp
tongs	putt
Matt	mitt
Watt	trap

as in <u>t</u>op

as in pu<u>tt</u>

_____

- - - - - - - - - - - -

_____

- - - - - - - - - - - -

_____

- - - - - - - - - - - -

_____

- - - - - - - - - - - -

_____

- - - - - - - - - - - -

_____

Dear Family Member,

Ask your child to cut out the two circles. Pin the smaller circle on top of the larger circle with a brass fastener. Ask your child to spin the smaller circle to make words. Have your child read the words he or she makes. Ask your child to copy the words on a sheet of paper. Another way to practice: Arrange the circles yourself and have your child read the words.

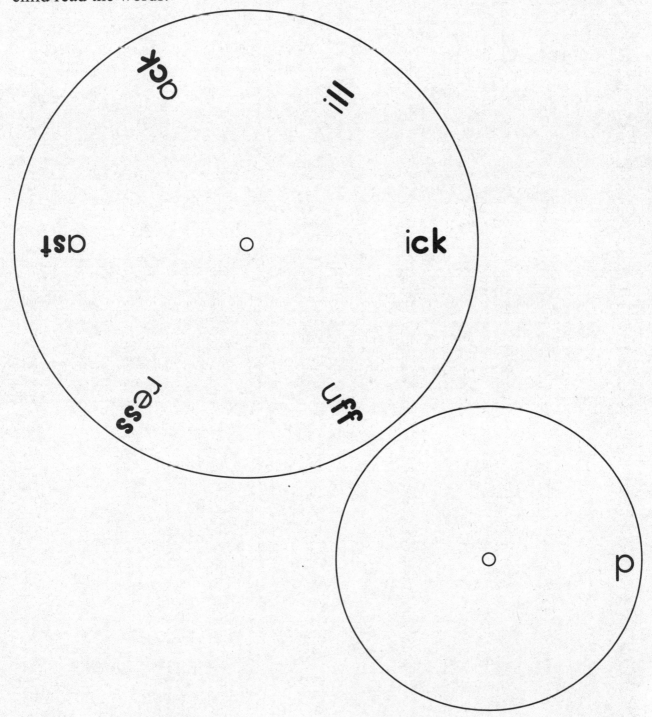

© 2013 Core Knowledge Foundation

Dear Family Member,

Ask your child to cut out the two circles. Pin the smaller circle on top of the larger circle with a brass fastener. Ask your child to spin the smaller circle to make words. Have your child read the words he or she makes. Ask your child to copy the words on a sheet of paper. Another way to practice: Arrange the circles yourself and have your child read the words.

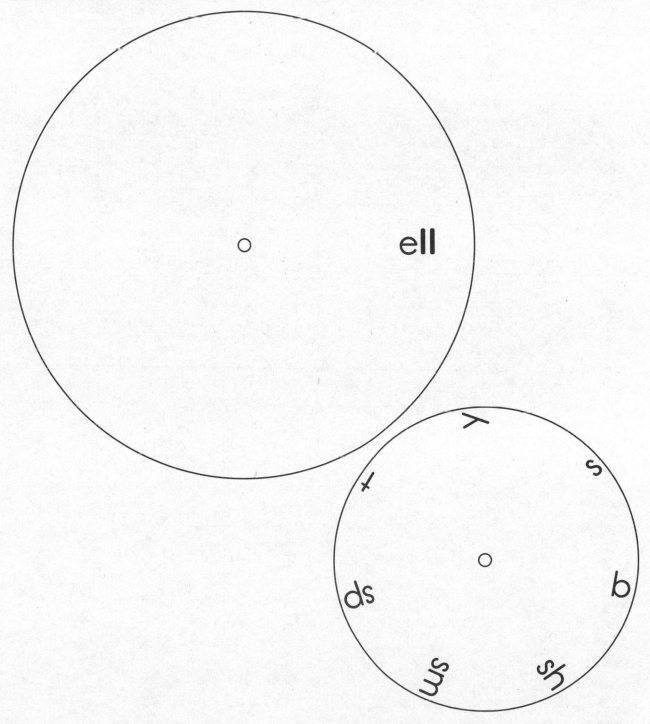

Dear Family Member,

This is a story your child has read at school. Encourage your child to read the story to you, and then talk about it together.

Max in the Mud

Max tra**ck**s mud on the de**ck**.

Sam's mom ye**ll**s, "Bad dog!"

Sam's mom has Sam get a mop.

Sam gets a mop

and mops up the mud.

Sam's mom sniffs Max.

Ug!

The dog smells bad!

Sam gets Max in the bath tub.

Sam's mom scrubs him.

Then, at last, Max smells fresh!

Dear Family Member,

   This is a story your child has read at school. Encourage your child to read the story to you, and then talk about it together.

The Band

Sam's dad is in a ja**zz** band.

That's him in the ba**ck**.

Chad's dad is in the band with him.

That's him on the drums.

Chad's bo**ss** is in the band, as we**ll**.

That's him on the left, in the hat.

Sam's dad plu**ck**s at his strings.

Chad's dad bangs on his drums.

The kids clap and ye**ll**.

The band is a big hit!

Name _____

PP7

Dear Family Member,

This is a story your child has read at school. Encourage your child to read the story to you, and then talk about it together. The tricky letters in the words are underlined in gray.

The Chick

Sam and Chad got up on a ro**ck**.

On top of the ro**ck** was a gu**ll**'s nest.

The gu**ll** had a chi**ck**.

The gu**ll** fed the chi**ck** a bit of fish.

Then the gu**ll** left.

The chi**ck** fell fr<u>o</u>m its nest.

Plop!

The chi**ck** got stu**ck** in a
cra**ck**.

Sam and Chad got the
chi**ck**.

Then Chad set it ba**ck** in
its nest.

Directions: Have students trace and copy the double-letter spellings. Encourage students to say the letter names while writing.

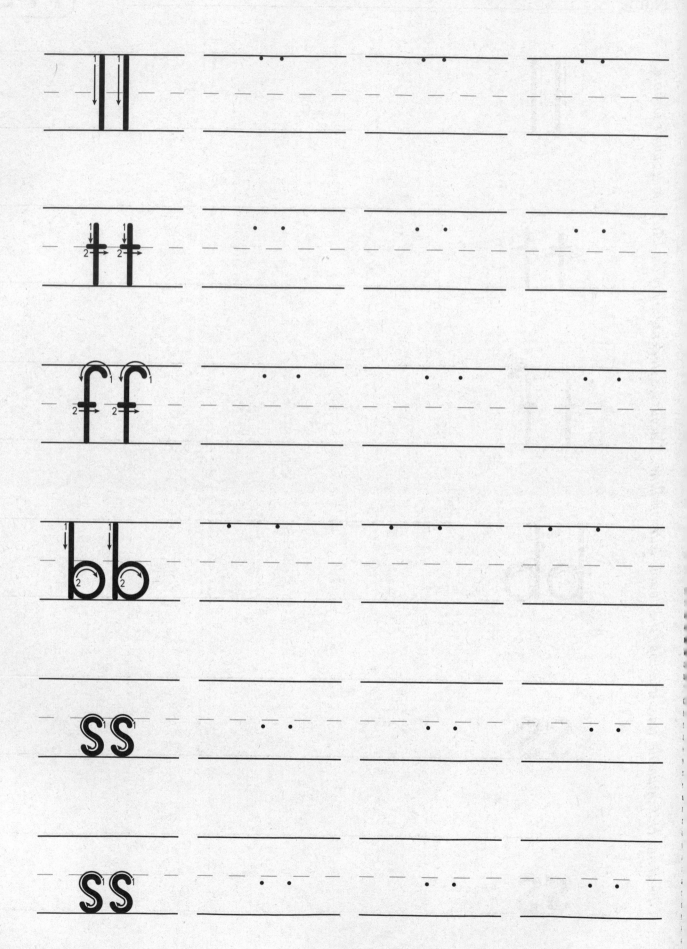

Directions: Have students trace and copy the double-letter spellings. Encourage students to say the letter names while writing.

c c

c k

d d

r r

n n

m m

c c

c k

d d

r r

n n

m m

Directions: Have students trace and copy the double-letter spellings. Encourage students to say the letter names while writing.

z z

z z

p p

p p

g g

g g

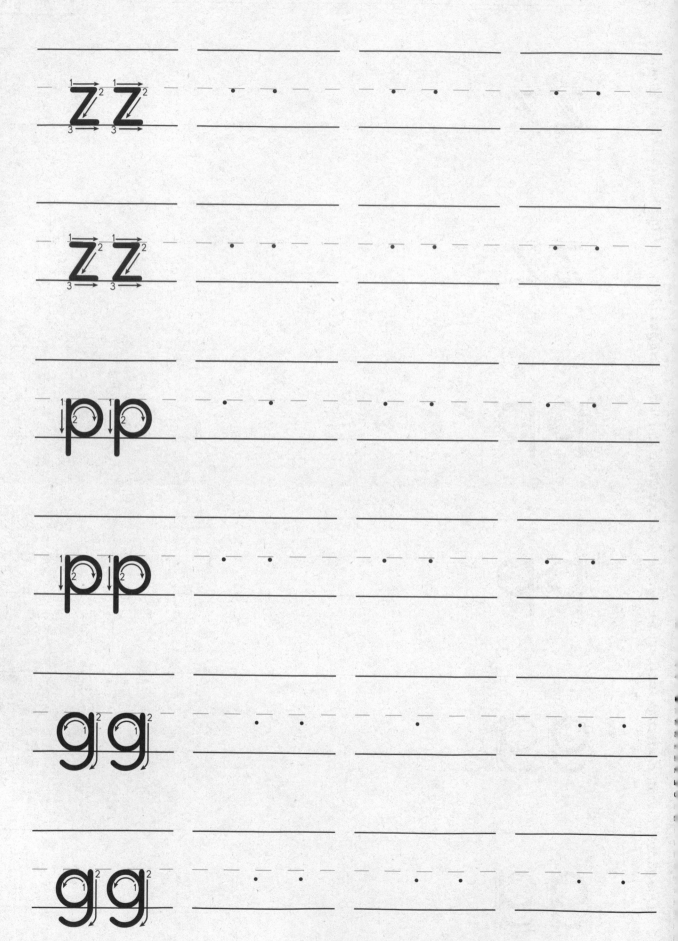

Directions: Have students write each word under its matching picture.

1. so**ck**s

_____

- - - - - - - - - - - - - - - - -

_____

2. ye**ll**

_____

- - - - - - - - - - - - - - - - -

_____

3. cl**iff**

_____

- - - - - - - - - - - - - - - - -

_____

4. grass

_____
- - - - - - - -
_____

_____
- - - - - - - -
_____

5. truck

_____
- - - - - - - -
_____

_____
- - - - - - - -
_____

6. bell

_____
- - - - - - - -
_____

_____
- - - - - - - -
_____

Directions: For each picture, have students circle the letters that spell the name of the depicted item. Students should then write the name of the item on the line.

	b / p	e / u	m / ll

	ch / b	a / i	ck / d

	b / p	i / e	ll / ff

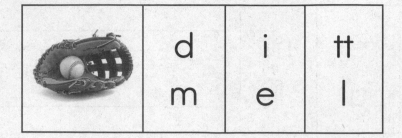

| | d m | i e | tt l | _____ _ _ _ _ _ _ _ _ _ _____ |

| | m d | u o | th ck | _____ _ _ _ _ _ _ _ _ _ _____ |

| | p y | e i | f ll | _____ _ _ _ _ _ _ _ _ _ _____ |

Directions: Have students circle the pronounced word and then copy it on the lines.

1. a**dd**   o**dd**

2. la**ck**   li**ck**

3. che**ss**   dre**ss**

4. gla**ss**   gra**ss**

5. mi**tt**   mat

6. mo**ss**   to**ss**

7. pre**ss** dre**ss**

8. bu**zz** fu**zz**

9. **inn** chin

10. sme**ll** fe**ll**

11. a**dd** o**dd**

12. e**gg** leg

Directions: Have students trace and copy the words. Encourage students to say the letter names while writing the words.

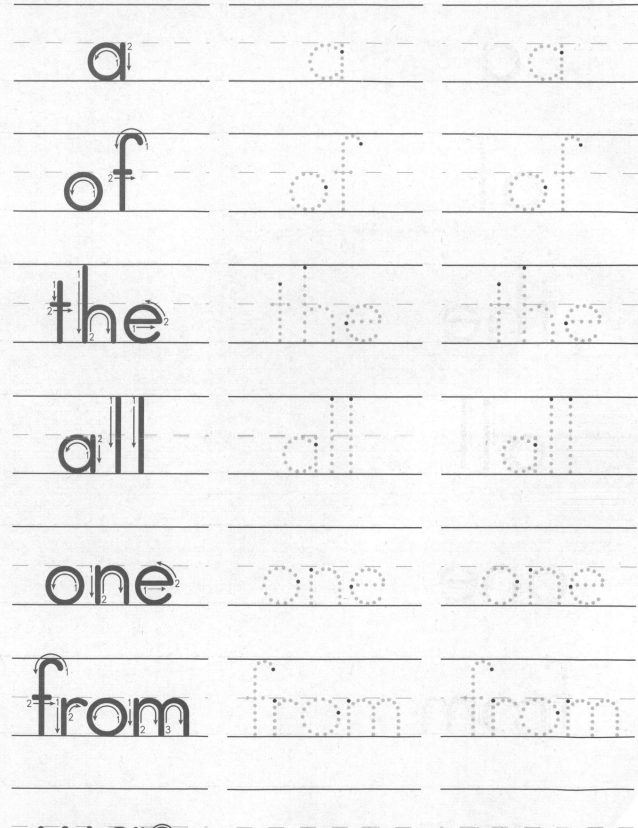

a

of

the

all

one

from

was

a

of

the

all

one

from

was

1. <u>one</u>   fr<u>o</u>m

Directions: Have students draw a line from each word on the left to the rhyming word on the right.

2. still   miss

3. strum   sun

4. fuzz   thrill

5. kiss   w<u>a</u>s

6. mess   puff

7. beg   fell

8. stuck   egg

9. stuff   less

10. shell   luck

CORE KNOWLEDGE LANGUAGE ARTS

SERIES EDITOR-IN-CHIEF
E. D. Hirsch, Jr.

PRESIDENT
Linda Bevilacqua

EDITORIAL STAFF
Carolyn Gosse, Senior Editor - Preschool
Khara Turnbull, Materials Development Manager
Michelle L. Warner, Senior Editor - Listening & Learning

Mick Anderson
Robin Blackshire
Maggie Buchanan
Paula Coyner
Sue Fulton
Sara Hunt
Erin Kist
Robin Luecke
Rosie McCormick
Cynthia Peng
Liz Pettit
Ellen Sadler
Deborah Samley
Diane Auger Smith
Sarah Zelinke

DESIGN AND GRAPHICS STAFF
Scott Ritchie, Creative Director

Kim Berrall
Michael Donegan
Liza Greene
Matt Leech
Bridget Moriarty
Lauren Pack

CONSULTING PROJECT MANAGEMENT SERVICES
ScribeConcepts.com

ADDITIONAL CONSULTING SERVICES
Ang Blanchette
Dorrit Green
Carolyn Pinkerton

ACKNOWLEDGMENTS

These materials are the result of the work, advice, and encouragement of numerous individuals over many years. Some of those singled out here already know the depth of our gratitude; others may be surprised to find themselves thanked publicly for help they gave quietly and generously for the sake of the enterprise alone. To helpers named and unnamed we are deeply grateful.

CONTRIBUTORS TO EARLIER VERSIONS OF THESE MATERIALS
Susan B. Albaugh, Kazuko Ashizawa, Nancy Braier, Kathryn M. Cummings, Michelle De Groot, Diana Espinal, Mary E. Forbes, Michael L. Ford, Ted Hirsch, Danielle Knecht, James K. Lee, Diane Henry Leipzig, Martha G. Mack, Liana Mahoney, Isabel McLean, Steve Morrison, Juliane K. Munson, Elizabeth B. Rasmussen, Laura Tortorelli, Rachael L. Shaw, Sivan B. Sherman, Miriam E. Vidaver, Catherine S. Whittington, Jeannette A. Williams

We would like to extend special recognition to Program Directors Matthew Davis and Souzanne Wright who were instrumental to the early development of this program.

SCHOOLS
We are truly grateful to the teachers, students, and administrators of the following schools for their willingness to field test these materials and for their invaluable advice: Capitol View Elementary, Challenge Foundation Academy (IN), Community Academy Public Charter School, Lake Lure Classical Academy, Lepanto Elementary School, New Holland Core Knowledge Academy, Paramount School of Excellence, Pioneer Challenge Foundation Academy, New York City PS 26R (The Carteret School), PS 30X (Wilton School), PS 50X (Clara Barton School), PS 96Q, PS 102X (Joseph O. Loretan), PS 104Q (The Bays Water), PS 214K (Michael Friedsam), PS 223Q (Lyndon B. Johnson School), PS 308K (Clara Cardwell), PS 333Q (Goldie Maple Academy), Sequoyah Elementary School, South Shore Charter Public School, Spartanburg Charter School, Steed Elementary School, Thomas Jefferson Classical Academy, Three Oaks Elementary, West Manor Elementary.

And a special thanks to the CKLA Pilot Coordinators Anita Henderson, Yasmin Lugo-Hernandez, and Susan Smith, whose suggestions and day-to-day support to teachers using these materials in their classrooms was critical.

CREDITS

ILLUSTRATORS AND IMAGE SOURCES